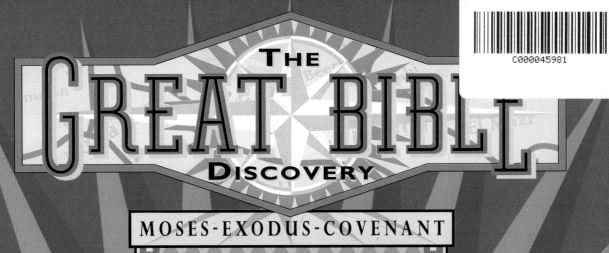

THE GREAT BIBLE DISCOVERY

MOSES-EXODUS-COVENANT

THE BIBLE IS A BEST-SELLER. IT IS ALSO ONE OF THE MASTER-WORKS OF WORLD LITERATURE - SO IMPORTANT THAT UNIVERSITIES TODAY TEACH 'NON-RELIGIOUS' BIBLE COURSES TO HELP STUDENTS WHO CHOOSE TO STUDY WESTERN LITERATURE.

THE BIBLE POSSESSES AN AMAZING POWER TO FASCINATE YOUNG AND OLD ALIKE.

ONE REASON FOR THIS UNIVERSAL APPEAL IS THAT IT DEALS WITH BASIC HUMAN LONGINGS, EMOTIONS, RELATIONSHIPS. 'ALL THE WORLD IS HERE.' ANOTHER REASON IS THAT SO MUCH OF THE BIBLE CONSISTS OF STORIES. THEY ARE FULL OF MEANING BUT EASY TO REMEMBER.

HERE ARE THOSE STORIES, PRESENTED SIMPLY AND WITH A MINIMUM OF EXPLANATION. WE HAVE LEFT THE TEXT TO SPEAK FOR ITSELF. GIFTED ARTISTS USE THE ACTION-STRIP TECHNIQUE TO BRING THE BIBLE'S DEEP MESSAGE TO READERS OF ALL AGES. THEIR DRAWINGS ARE BASED ON INFORMATION FROM ARCHAEOLOGICAL DISCOVERIES COVERING FIFTEEN CENTURIES.

AN ANCIENT BOOK - PRESENTED FOR THE PEOPLE OF THE SECOND MILLENNIUM. A RELIGIOUS BOOK - PRESENTED FREE FROM THE INTERPRETATION OF ANY PARTICULAR CHURCH. A UNIVERSAL BOOK - PRESENTED IN A FORM THAT ALL MAY ENJOY.

M publishing
CARLISLE, UK

4

Moses was the man God used to liberate the people of
Israel and to give them God's law. By any standards, the man who
turned a rabble of slaves into a nation was a remarkable leader.
Moses is the greatest figure in the Old Testament.
His story displays a pattern very like what we have
seen in the life of Joseph. God's hand can be seen
in what may often seem like disaster. Brought up
among worshippers of many gods, Moses was cared for by a mother
who taught him about the God of Abraham, Isaac and Jacob.
Destined to lead a nation, he was educated as a prince of Egypt.
Losing the luxury of his place at the Egyptian court, he learned how
to live in the desert.

The disasters that came upon Egypt when the Pharaoh refused
to let the Hebrews go can be 'explained' in various
ways. God's people remembered them as signs of
the power of the God of Israel. Not even the
mightiest nation in the world could stand against
him.

The word 'exodus' means 'going out'. Israel never
forgot the exodus from Egypt. They
commemorated it each year in the Passover festival, a
constant reminder of God's power to deliver. In the
twentieth century many poor and disadvantaged people have seen
it as a symbol of God's concern for the poor and helpless.
The exodus was not a reward for a people who had obeyed God's
law. It was after they had been delivered from slavery that God
offered to make Israel his own . From then on they were joined by
the Sinai covenant. The Torah (the Law) they received then was
almost like a wedding ring signifying the union.
The story of Israel's journey through the desert tells of God's
faithfulness to them, rather than theirs to him. Guided, fed,
protected by him, they would reach the land God had promised to
Abraham.

EXODUS
LEVITICUS
NUMBERS
DEUTERONOMY

MOSES-EXODUS-COVENANT

4

First published as *Découvrir la Bible* 1983

First edition © Librairie Larousse 1983
English translation © Daan Retief Publishers 1990
24-volume series adaptation by Mike Jacklin © Knowledge Unlimited 1994
This edition © OM Publishing 1995

01 00 99 98 97 96 95   7 6 5 4 3 2 1

OM Publishing is an imprint of Send the Light Ltd.,
P.O. Box 300, Carlisle, Cumbria CA3 0QS, U.K.

Series editor: D. Roy Briggs
English translation: Bethan Uden
Introductions: Peter Cousins

British Library Cataloguing in Publication Data
A catalogue record for this book is available from the British Library
ISBN 1-85078-208-3

Printed in Singapore by Tien Wah Press (Pte) Ltd.

MOSES

IN EGYPT IT IS MANY YEARS SINCE JOSEPH AND ALL HIS BROTHERS DIED, AND THE ISRAELITES HAVE GROWN IN NUMBER.

ARIO : Etienne DAHLER
ING: Carlo MARCELLO

THE FINE THINGS JOSEPH DID HAVE BEEN FORGOTTEN, AND THE PHARAOH FEELS THREATENED BY THE HEBREW PEOPLE.

THEY LIVE ON THE EDGE OF THE COUNTRY...

...AND THEIR NUMBERS INCREASE SO QUICKLY!

THEIR LIFE'S TOO EASY. WE MUST MAKE IT HARDER FOR THEM.

7

MIRIAM RAN TO HER MOTHER.

THE BOY GREW...

THE YEARS PASSED...

YOUR STUDIES ARE FINISHED, MOSES. I'VE TAUGHT YOU ALL THE WISDOM OF EGYPT. YOU'LL DO VERY WELL AT THE PALACE.

FIRST LET ME GO AND GREET MY FAMILY.

MOSES, MY SON!

MOTHER... I C[A] STAY LONG

I'VE HAD BETTER LUCK THAN MY BROTHER HEBREWS. HOW HARD THEY HAVE TO WORK!

BUT WHAT ARE THOSE CRIES?

TO THANK HIM FOR HELPING HIS DAUGHTERS, JETHRO, PRIEST OF MIDIAN, INVITED MOSES TO EAT WITH THEM.

STAY WITH ME AS LONG AS YOU LIKE... MARRY ONE OF MY DAUGHTERS.

YEARS PASSED. ZIPPORAH, ONE OF JETHRO'S DAUGHTERS, GAVE HIM TWO SONS.

GERSHOM!* DON'T GO TOO FAR!

*First name, meaning 'A stranger among us'.

THE PHARAOH IS DEAD! SOME MERCHANTS TOLD US JUST NOW.

ARE YOU SURE?

GOD OF ABRAHAM, ISAAC, AND JACOB, HEAR THE CRY OF YOUR PEOPLE WHO GROAN IN SLAVERY.

YES, AND THEY SAY THAT THE NEW PHARAOH'S EVEN HARDER ON YOUR BROTHERS.

14

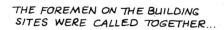

FROM NOW ON YOU'LL NOT BE GIVEN ANY STRAW...

BUT YOU MUST STILL MAKE THE SAME NUMBER OF BRICKS!

A FEW DAYS LATER...

YOU'RE NOT MAKING AS MANY BRICKS, SO... THE FEWER THE BRICKS, THE MORE LASHES OF THE WHIP!

BUT WE CAN'T DO IT!

YOU JUST BAC TO W

MOSES, IS THIS THE WAY YOU SET YOUR PEOPLE FREE FROM SLAVERY?

LORD, WHY DO YOU LET YOUR PEOPLE SUFFER LIK THIS? WHY DID YOU SEND ME?

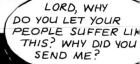

18

AT SUNRISE THE PHARAOH WENT TO THE NILE TO BATHE...

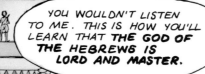

YOU WOULDN'T LISTEN TO ME. THIS IS HOW YOU'LL LEARN THAT **THE GOD OF THE HEBREWS IS LORD AND MASTER.**

AARON STRIKE TH IN THE R

AT ONCE THE WATER IN THE NILE BECAME LIKE BLOOD...

THAT'S NO PROOF! MY MAGICIANS CAN DO THE SAME THING!

BECAUSE THE PHARAOH RE STUBBORN, A SECOND PLAG STRUCK EGYPT.

PRAY TO YOUR GOD TO TAKE AWAY THESE FROGS, AND I'LL LET YOUR PEOPLE GO.

BY THE NEXT DAY ALL THE FROGS WERE DE BUT THE PHARAOH DIDN'T KE HIS PROMISE. THEN SWARMS OF GNATS FILLED THE WHOLE COUNT

MOSES
Part two

SCENARIO: Etienne DAHLER
DRAWING: Carlo MARCELLO

MOSES, WHY DID YOU LEAD US OUT OF EGYPT? TO DIE IN THE DESERT?

I'D RATHER WORK FOR THE EGYPTIANS.

BE QUIET! STOP COMPLAINING. THE LORD WON'T ABANDON US!

LET'S CAMP HERE TONIGHT. TOMORROW MORNING WE'LL ATTACK THEM.

LIFT UP YOUR STAFF; STRETC OUT YOUR HAN OVER THE SEA, AND DIVIDE IT IN TWO.

GOD'S PROMISED US A LAND... WE MUST GO THAT WAY!

THE WORST'S STILL TO COME.

THE LORD HELPED US TO CROSS THE SEA. HE CAN ALSO TAKE US THROUGH THE DESERT!

THEY WALKED FOR THREE DAYS WITHOUT FINDING WATER...

...AT LAST, A WATER-HOLE...

IT'S BITTER!* IT'S NOT FIT TO DRINK!

...ed the place MARAH (bitterness).

AND THAT EVENING...

... EVERYONE HAD ENOUGH TO EAT.

AT DAWN...

LOOK! WHAT'S THAT?*

* In Hebrew, Man hu.

IT'S MANNA, THE BREAD GOD WILL GIVE US EVERY DAY UNTIL WE REACH THE PROMISED LAND.

EACH YOU'LL ONLY AS YO NO M

LOOK! THE MANNA I'D SAVED... FULL OF WORMS!

EVE WE DE OI

HOURS PASSED...
WHEN MOSES'
ARMS GREW TIRED,
AARON HELD THEM UP...

THE LORD IS OUR STRE[...]
IF MOSES HOLDS O[...]
WE WILL TOO.

BY NIGHTFALL THE
AMALEKITES WERE
BEATEN.

YOU GAVE US THE VICTORY,
LORD. FROM NOW ON THIS
PLACE WILL BE CALLED
ADONAI NISSI *!

THE ENEMY SAID,
'I'LL CHASE THEM, I'LL DE[...]
THEM!
LORD, YOUR HAND
SCATTERED THE ENEM[...]

* The Lord is my Banner.

THE NEXT DAY MOSES BUILT AN ALTAR OF TWELVE STONES, ONE FOR EACH TRIBE, AND MADE PEACE-OFFERINGS.

MOSES POURED THE BLOOD OF TH[E] SACRIFICED ANIMAL OVER TH[E]

... THEN HE TOOK THE TABLETS AND READ TO THE PEOPLE...

THE WORD OF THE LORD!

MOSES SPRINKLED THE PEOPLE...

THIS IS THE **BLOOD OF THE COVENANT** THAT THE LORD'S MADE WITH YOU!

WE'LL DO EVERYTHING THAT THE LORD COMMANDS.

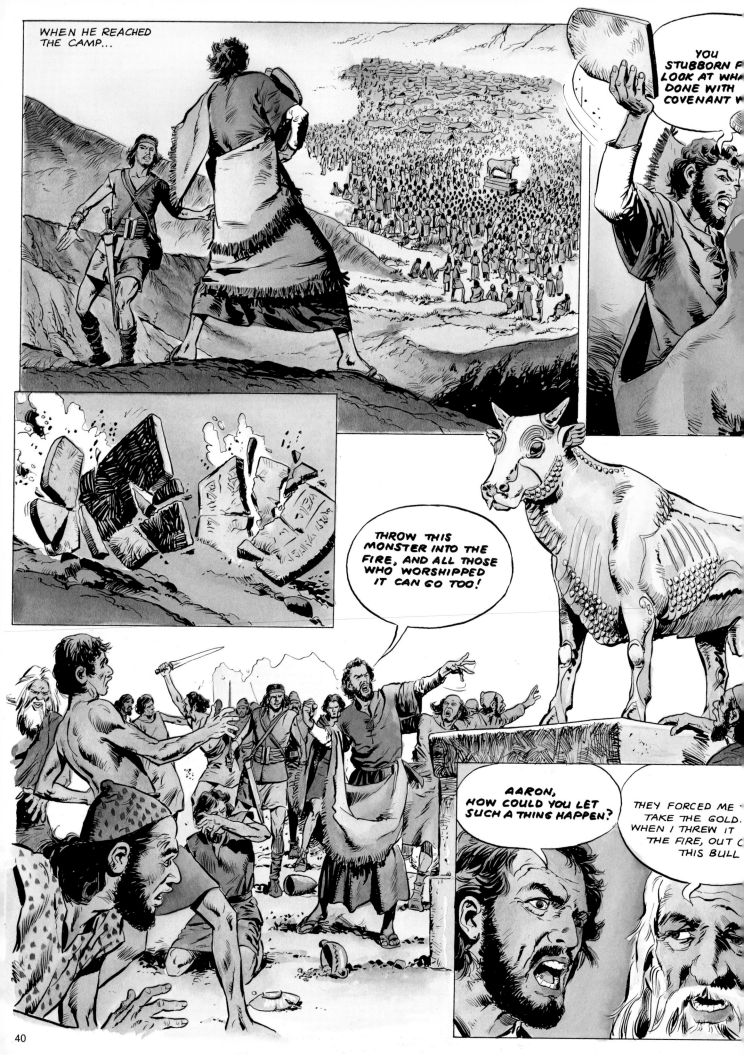

THEY PUT THE BOX WITH THE TABLETS OF THE LAW IN THE HOLIEST PLACE.

LORD, HERE'S YOUR HOME. MAY YOUR GLORY BE HERE!

A CURTAIN WAS HUNG IN FRONT. ONLY THE HIGH PRIEST COULD GO BEHIND IT.

IN THIS HOLY PLACE LET PRAYER GO UP TO YOU LIKE INCENSE IN A SACRIFICE OF PRAISE.

AARON, YOU MUST BE ANOINTED AS A PRIEST.

THEN ALL THE P
SAW THE CLOUD
THE ENTRANCE
TENT AND THE G
OF THE L

...DAY, WHEN MOSES CAME
...OF THE TENT...

BRING ME ONE
...AN FROM EACH OF
...THE TWELVE
TRIBES.

THE TRIBE OF
LEVI WAS NOT
COUNTED,
BECAUSE IT HAD
BEEN CHOSEN TO
SERVE IN THE
TENT.

COUNT THE CHILDREN OF ISRAEL. MAKE
A LIST OF ALL THE MEN MORE THAN
20 YEARS OLD, FIT TO CARRY ARMS.

WHY ARE YOU DOING THAT?
TO CONQUER THE LAND OF CANAAN?
BUT WHOM WILL YOU PUT AT THE
HEAD OF THE ARMY?

I'M DOING WHAT
GOD TOLD ME
TO DO.

WE'VE
COUNTED ALL THE
MEN!

GOOD...
HOLD YOURSELVES
READY. WHEN THE CLOUD
RISES ABOVE THE TENT,
WE LEAVE.

SEVEN DAYS LATER, MIRIAM WAS HEALED. THE PEOPLE LEFT HAZEROTH AND CAMPED IN THE WILDERNESS OF PARAN.

MOSES CALLED THE CHIEFS OF THE TRIBES TOGETHER...

WE'RE GETTING NEAR TO CANAAN. YOU MUST CHOOSE A MAN FROM EACH TRIBE TO EXPLORE THE LAND WHICH THE LORD'S GIVING TO US.

EXPLORE THE LAND OF CANA... FIND OUT HOW MANY PEOPLE LIVE THERE, AND HOW STRONG TOWNS ARE... MAY THE LOR... GUARD AND BLESS YOU.

REUBEN

GAD

SIMEON

JUDAH

ISSACHAR

BENJAMIN

DAN

MANASSEH

NAPHTALI

ASHER

EPHRAIM

ZEBULUN

AND THE TWELVE SET OFF FOR THE PROMISED LAND.